CARS II

This book belongs to:

Alfa Romeo 1600 GTV Junior

This is a car from 1975. Alfa's red-painted cars were familiar at race circuits as long ago as 1924. Their later sports cars have always appealed to enthusiasts. The 1600 GTs were styled by several designers but Bertone is thought to be the best.

*I-Spy for **20***

Alfa Romeo 33 Sportwagon

This is the estate version of the Alfa 33 and it was launched in 1987. It is powered by the 1.7-litre boxer engine and offers 0-60 mph (0-96 km/h) performance in under 10 seconds so it can be described as a true sports estate. It offers good load-carrying space but has a high rear sill.

*I-Spy for **10***

Alfa Romeo 75

This sporting saloon is available in three engine options: 1.6 litre; 2-litre Twin Spark; and 3 litre. It is rear-wheel drive and the gearbox is also situated in the rear axle to spread the weight. The Twin Spark returns 0-60 mph (0-96 km/h) in just over 9 seconds while, at a constant 75 mph (120 km/h), 34 mpg (12.1 km/l) is possible. What does Twin Spark indicate?

____

*I-Spy for **10** — double with answer*

Alfa Romeo 155

The 155 is the first Alfa Romeo to be built in its entirety since the famous Italian company was taken over by Fiat. The 155 is a 4-door saloon with parts in common with the Fiat Tempra and Lancia Dedra although it was styled by Alfa Romeo. There are three Alfa-built engines, the 1.8-litre Twin Spark, the 2-litre Twin Spark, and the 2.5-litre V6 which develops 165 bhp.

*I-Spy for **10***

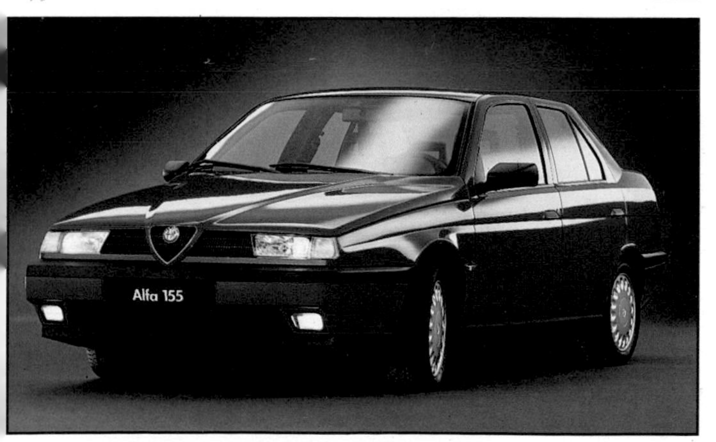

Alvis TD21

Alvis were famous in the 1920s for their superb sports cars which were often used in competitions and trials, such as the 'London-Land's End'. The firm was credited with introducing front-wheel drive in 1928. This elegant 1963 TD21 had a 3-litre, 6-cylinder engine giving a top speed of 105 mph (169 km/h).

*I-Spy for **30***

Armstrong Siddeley Star Sapphire

Armstrong Siddeley, formed in 1919, was one of Britain's most distinguished marques. The post-war Star Sapphire was the last model that the group produced. It was a luxury saloon capable of achieving a standing ¼ mile (400 m) in only 18.2 seconds.

*I-Spy for **30***

Aston Martin DB5 Volante

The DB5 series was immortalized in the James Bond films *Goldfinger* and *Thunderball*. Production ran from 1963 to 1965. Th 3995 cc engine developed 282 bhp at 5500 rpm. The price new for a Drophead Coupé was £4570.00. What does rpm stand for?

*I-Spy for **20***
Double with answer

Aston Martin Virage Volante 2+2

This 2+2 version of the two-seat Volante was built in response to customer demand. Powered by Aston Martin's own 5.4-litre, 32-valve, V8 engine, the company claims that it is one of the most powerful 'lead-free' units in the world, delivering 330 bhp. What does bhp stand for?

*I-Spy for **20***
Double with answer

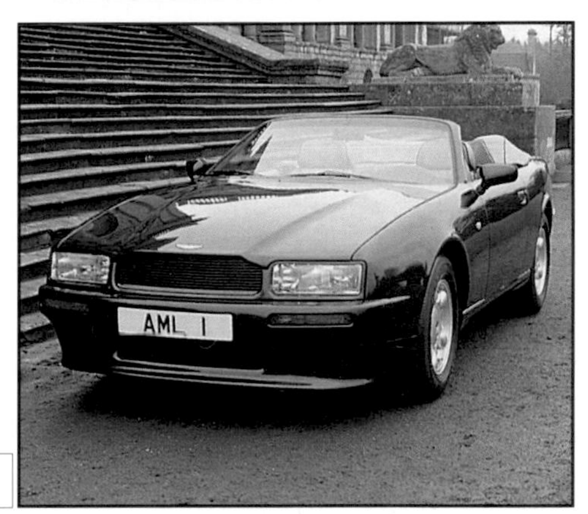

Audi 80

Externally, the 1992 Audi 80s differ in only subtle ways from their predecessors but there is now a new, refined V6 engine option as well as a larger boot, and a redesigned suspension. The top of the range is the 2.8 E generating 174 bhp and it is available in front-wheel drive or Quattro versions.
What does the name 'Quattro' indicate?
*I-Spy for **5** — double with answer*

Audi 100

Among the engine options available for the latest Audi 100 is a 2.5-litre, 5-cylinder diesel unit which is broadly based on the 2.3 petrol engine. It is the first production car on the market ever to achieve a 65 per cent fuel consumption cut and yet can still attain speeds of over 120 mph (193 km/h).
*I-Spy for **5***

Audi 100 Quattro Est

There are two engines available for the 100 Quattro Estate: either the 2.3-litre, 5-cylinder unit which produces 133 bhp or the 2.8-litre V6 developing 174 bhp. With the new estate, it has been Audi's intention to create an individualistic executive estate with good load space. ABS is standard.
*I-Spy for **5***

Audi Coupé Quattro

The Audi Coupé range includes the 2.0E; the 2.8E with the same V6 engine available in the new Audi 100 and 80 ranges; and the Coupé S2 with its 220 bhp, 154 mph (248 km/h) in quattro drive. There is also the 2.3E with a choice of manual and automatic transmission.
*I-Spy for **5** for any coupé*
Double for the S2

Austin A30

Originally known as the Austin 7, it is now more familiar as the A30. It was Austin's first attempt at monocoque construction. In 1957, the larger-engined A35 was announced. It was this 948 cc unit that powered the 'Frog-eye' Sprite.
*I-Spy for **20***

Austin Healey Sprite

This small two-seater gets its nickname of 'Frog-eye' from the appearance of the round headlamps mounted high up on the bonnet. The A35 engine developed just 42.5 bhp. Despite its modest performance, it still holds a lot of appeal for sports car enthusiasts.
*I-Spy for **20***

Bentley Continental R

This is the first all-new version of the marque to be launched since 1952, and the 2-seater coupé body has been developed specifically for Bentley. The 6.75-litre, turbo-charged power unit, driving through a 4-speed automatic gearbox takes this luxurious sports coupé from 0-60 mph (0-96 km/h) in a mere 6.6 seconds.
*I-Spy for **20***

Bentley Continental S1

Introduced in 1957 as the world's most expensive production car, the saloon cost £5070.00 when an Austin A35 was only £573.00. Coachbuilders were either Park Ward or H J Mulliner. The 6-cylinder, 5-litre car was ideal for high-speed, luxury touring.
*I-Spy for **30***

BMW 316i

This car has been designed to appeal to private owners and to the company car market. The 4-cylinder, 1596 cc engine delivers 100 bhp and returns an average fuel consumption of 35.8 mpg (12.7 km/l). There is an optional four-speed automatic gearbox available.

I-Spy for ***10***

BMW 318i Convertible

In 1991, the classic BMW convertible became available with a new 1.8-litre engine, offering improved fuel economy and cheaper insurance. There are thirteen possible body colours to combine with a choice of black, brown, or blue hood material.

I-Spy for ***15***

BMW 518i

The BMW 518i combines the body and chassis of the 5 series with an efficient 1796 cc, fuel-injected,115 bhp engine which returns an average fuel consumption on unleaded fuel of 34.9 mpg (12.4 km/l). It is fitted with a catalytic converter as standard. BMW also claims that running costs of this car are about half as much as its predecessor.

*I-Spy for **10***

BMW 850i

Designed with comfort, safety, and style in mind, this latest BMW coupé also has a very 'slippery' shape. The 5-litre, 12-cylinder engine driving through a 6-speed manual gearbox takes the car to an electronically limited top speed of 155 mph (250 km/h).

*I-Spy for **20***

Bristol

There are two body types and three models in the current Bristol range of luxury cars. The Britannia and Brigand are full 4-seater saloons and the Brigand benefits from turbocharging. The Beaufighter is a 4-seater convertible. The cars are fitted with 5.9-litre V-8 engines
*I-Spy for **20***
Double for all three

Caterham Super 7

In 1991 Caterham changed the engine of its car for the first time in thirty years. The new unit is a 16-valve, 2-litre Vauxhall engine, fitted with twin Weber carburettors, to deliver 175 bhp and a 0-60 mph (0-96 km/h) time of under 5 seconds. Fitting this large engine has been achieved without changing the overall dimensions of the car.
*I-Spy for **20***

Citroën XM Estate

The luxury XM estate has been designed with performance, safety, comfort, handling, and spaciousness in mind. The unique, computer-controlled Hydractive suspension system is self-levelling and height adustable. There is a choice of three models: the 2.0-litre injection, the 2.1-litre turbo-diesel, and the 3.0-litre V6 Si with a top speed of 135 mph (217 km/h).

*I-Spy for **10***

Citroën ZX

With the ZX, the famous French car company claims to have set out to produce the best car in its class. There are currently four models in the range: the Reflex and Advantage have 1.4-litre engines, the Aura is a 1.6, and the Volcane offers a 1.9-litre, fuel-injected engine delivering 130 bhp.

*I-Spy for **5***

Daihatsu Applause 1.6GXi

This car has the appearance of a saloon and the lifting tailgate of a hatchback. It is powered by an all-alloy, 16-valve, fuel-injected engine which gives 0-60 mph (0-96 km/h) in under 10 seconds yet returns an average fuel economy of over 40 mpg (14.2 km/l).
I-Spy for ***10***

Daihatsu Charade

There are five models in the Charade range. The most economical is the 3-cylinder, 1.0-litre, turbo-diesel which at a steady 56 mph (90 km/h) returns over 78 mpg (28 km/l). There are two models powered by the 1.3-litre, 4-cylinder petrol engine but the GTti claims to be the fastest 1.0-litre production car in the world with a 0-60 mph (0-96 km/h) of under 8 seconds.
I-Spy for ***10***

Daihatsu Fourtrak

There are four models in this range of 4-wheel drive estates, from the 2.8 DL and the 2-litre petrol GX to the Turbo Diesel TDL and TDX. Every model is fitted with a 5-speed gearbox which also offers a second reduction ratio giving effectively ten forward and two reverse gears.
I-Spy for ***10***

Ferrari 512 TR

The latest Pininfarina body design is matched with technical improvements to reduce exhaust emissions and to improve handling and safety. The more powerful engine has been derived directly from the F40's 3.0-litre, V8, twin-turbo unit and gives the car a top speed of 194.5 mph (313 km/h) and 0-62 mph (0-100 km/h) performance of 4.8 seconds.
*I-Spy for **50***

Fiat Tempra 1.8 ie SX Station Wagon

This estate is built on a version of the Tempra saloon's platform. Like other Fiat estates, it has the horizontally split tailgate, the lower section folding down to form a shelf. It is powered by a 1.8-litre, 110 bhp engine which returns over 28 mpg (10 km/l) even in urban driving.
*I-Spy for **5***

Fiat Tipo 2.0 ie 16v

This is a 5-door, 5-seater hatchback in which every outside body panel has been galvanized for anti-corrosion protection. The 1995 cc engine is able to run on unleaded fuel and has a 3-way catalytic converter. It delivers 148 bhp to take the car to a top speed of 128 mph (206 km/h) where legally allowed.
*I-Spy for **10***

Fiat Croma

This is Fiat's top-of-the-range luxury, 5-door saloon. It comes in three models: the 2.0 CHT has a twin-choke carburettor; the 2.0 i.e. offers electronic fuel injection; and there is also a turbo-charged version. The CHT returns a fuel economy of 39.2 mpg (13.9 km/l) at 75 mph (120 km/h) while the 2.0 Turbo i.e. can achieve a top speed of 134 mph (215 km/h).
*I-Spy for **15***

Ford Consul Capri

Mechanically the same as the Classic, the Consul Capri was one of Britain's most striking-looking cars of the period, owing much in style to the American 'glamour' cars. With its 1340 cc engine, it was underpowered but was stil capable of a top speed of 81 mph (130 km/h).

I-Spy for ***20***

Ford Escort XR3i

The latest XR3i is available in both 105 and 130 bhp versions, and these 16-valve, (code-named 'Zeta') engines have been designed specifically to operate with a catalyst. Among the car's interior fittings are new-design, wrap-around, high-back sports seating for the driver and front passenger.

I-Spy for ***15***

Ford Escort RS 2000

Powered by a 2-litre, 150 bhp, 16-valve, twin-cam engine, the RS 2000 is a potent road-going Escort. It has a top speed of 129 mph (208 km/h) and will reach 60 mph (96 km/h) from a standing start in just 8 seconds. The newly developed 5-speed gearbox has synchromesh on reverse gear. ABS is standard.

I-Spy for ***10***

Ford Granada

The Granada luxury range includes 4-door, booted saloons as well as 5-door models, and both versions are also available in the higher-specification Scorpio range. There is even a model specifically tailored for taxi use. There is a choice of engines from the 2.0-litre EFi to the 2.9 24-valve Cosworth capable of 140 mph (225 km/h).

I-Spy for ***15***

Ford Mustang Mach I

When it was introduced in 1964, the Ford Mustang was a sensational success, selling over 500 000 in the first eighteen months. The Mach 1 was the most expensive, and one with Ram Air Induction covered the ¼ mile (400 m) in 13.9 seconds.

I-Spy for ***20***

Ford Orion Encore

The Encore is a Special Edition of the classic family or business saloon. There is a choice of either a 1.4-litre or a 1.6-litre engine, and both are able to run on leaded or unleaded fuel. The car is available either in red or blue metallic finishes and comes with a number of features as standard which are often regarded as optional extras. ABS, however, is an extra.

I-Spy for ***5***

Ford Sierra Chasseur

There are three models in the Special Edition Chasseur versions of the well-known Sierra range. There is the Sapphire Chasseur, a sportingly styled saloon; the hatchback Sierra Chasseur; and the well-equipped load carrier, the estate version. All are powered by the 1.8-litre CVH engine which is able to run on leaded and unleaded petrol.

I-Spy for ***5***

Ford Zodiac Hyline

Another of the Mk 2 Ford saloons, the Zodiac was the luxury version of the Consul and Zephyr. It boasted a 2.5-litre straight 6 engine producing 109 bhp. This car was surely one of the finest, fast executive cars of its time.

I-Spy for ***30***

Honda Accord

There are two models and three engine specifications in the Accord range. The sports estate is known as the Aerodeck and has the same 2.2-litre, 16-valve, fuel-injected engine as the top-of-the-range 2.2i saloon. The 2.2i also boasts Honda's 4-wheel steer system, leather upholstery, and air conditioning.

I-Spy for ***5***

Honda Civic

There are five versions of the 3-door car and two saloons in the Civic range, with 1.4-litre, and 1.6-litre engine options all with 16-valve technology. Safety, economy, and exhaust emission levels have all been taken into consideration with the 'airbag' driver restraint on the VEi and the lean-burn engine capable of 63 mpg (22.3 km/l).

I-Spy for ***5***

Honda Concerto

The 5-door hatchback version offers a choice of four models: 1.5i, 1.6i, 1.6i-16, and 1.6i-SE. There is also a 4-door saloon which offers the three 1.6 engine types. All have power-assisted steering and the higher specification versions have ABS fitted as standard. What does ABS stand for?

____

I-Spy for ***5***
Double with answer

Honda Legend

The Legend comes in saloon and coupé versions, both powered by a 3.2-litre V6 engine which develops over 200 bhp. The car incorporates new safety features including the so-called 'supplemental restraint system', or 'air bag' on the driver's side. ABS, air conditioning, and cruise control are all standard.
*I-Spy for **10***

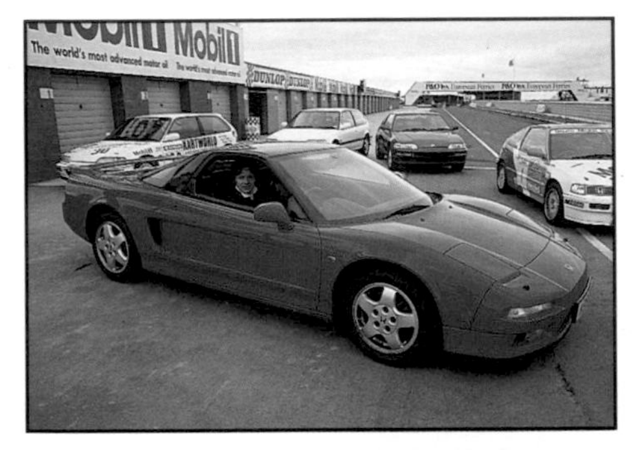

Honda NSX

The 3-litre, 24-valve, V6 power unit fitted to this race-bred two-seater develops 270 bhp, and comes with either manual or automatic gearbox. The strikingly styled body is constructed from aluminium to reduce weight and improve economy. Leather seats, cruise control, and ABS are standard.
*I-Spy for **20***

Hyundai Lantra

The 4-door Lantra saloon falls between the Ford Escort Orion and the Sierra Sapphire in dimensions. It is powered by a 1.6-litre, 16-valve, fuel-injected engine which develops up to 112 bhp. There are GLSi and CDi models, both with choice of manual or automatic transmission.
*I-Spy for **10***

Isuzu Trooper LWB

There are thirteen models of 4-wheel drive off-road vehicles to choose from in the Trooper range, and there is either a 2.6-litre fuel-injection petrol engine or a 2.8-litre turbo-diesel unit. The long-wheel-base versions have five doors and come in either 'Duty' or 'Citation' models. Look out for the central window.

*I-Spy for **10** for the LWB*

Jaguar Sovereign

Leather upholstery, burr walnut veneers with hand-applied matchwood inlays, full air conditioning, and electronic cruise control combine with Jaguar's distinctive styling to make the Sovereign a prestigious member of the Jaguar range. It is powered by either a 24-valve 3.2-litre engine or a 4-litre unit.

*I-Spy for **10***

Jaguar XJ220

At the time of its launch, in October 1991, the XJ220 was the world's fastest production car capable of speeds of over 212 mph (341 km/h) and 0-60 mph (0-96 km/h) acceleration in less than 4 seconds. This is achieved by the race-bred 3.5-litre twin turbo V-6 engine which develops 542 bhp. The dramatic styling and refined interior add to the car's uniqueness.

*I-Spy for **50***

Jaguar XJS V12 Convertible

The 5.3-litre, V-12 engine in the XJS Convertible powers the car, almost silently, through automatic transmission to a top speed of 143 mph (230 km/h) where legally permitted. At the touch of a button, the tailore hood and pillarless rear windows close to provide fixed-head coupé comfort.

*I-Spy for **20***

Kia Pride

This Korean-built, low-priced 'super-mini' comes in three models, all hatchbacks: the 3-door 1.1 L with its 1139 cc, 53-bhp engine; and the 1.3 LX in either 3- or 5-door options, with a 60-bhp engine and 5-speed gearbox. Interestingly, the larger-engined version offers better fuel economy, of 38.7 mpg (13.72 km/l) at 75 mph (120 km/h).
I-Spy for ***15***

Lada Samara

The Russian-built Samara range of low-priced, front-wheel-drive hatchbacks offers a choice of 1.1-, 1.3-, and 1.5-litre four-cylinder engines which all run on unleaded petrol. There are 3- and 5-door body styles as well as three levels of specification. The 1.5-litre model claims a top speed of more than 100 mph (160 km/h).
I-Spy for ***10***

Lagonda

The company was always well known for its sports cars. Later Lagondas were designed by W O Bentley. The V12, introduced in 1937, was considered to be one of his best designs. The engine could power the car to a top speed of 101 mph (163 km/h).
I-Spy for ***50***

Lancia Delta HF integrale

This is a 4-wheel drive performance car with a range of technical innovations as well as new styling. It is powered by a 2-litre, fuel-injected, turbocharged engine which develops 210 bhp and can hasten the car from 0-62 mph (0-100 km/h) in a mere 5.7 seconds and on to a top speed of 137 mph (220 km/h) where permitted.

*I-Spy for **20***

Lancia Thema

The Thema executive saloon was first introduce in 1984. The classic desig offers a choice of two engines — the 2.0-litre 16 valve developing 150 bhp and the 2.0-litre 16-valve turbo. The turbo-charged (water-cooled) car reache a top speed of 140 mph (225 km/h) and gives 0-62 mph (0-100 km/h) performance of just 7 seconds. Both cars run on lead-free petrol.

*I-Spy for **15***

Lotus Elan Hardtop

To the highly acclaimed pair of Elan sports cars, Lotus Cars of Norwich have added the option of a removal hardtop — available during 1992. The hardtop features double-skinned composite construction with an integral heated rear window, interior courtesy lighting, and a grey-finish interior.

*I-Spy for **20***

Lotus Esprit

There are two models: the Esprit SE, with its 264 bhp, 2.2-litre, 16-valve, charge-cooled unit; and the Esprit with a 215 bhp, turbo-charged engine. There have been significant improvements in cabin space, and the external modifications have led to reductions in drag and lift, so that the SE now achieves a top speed of 165 mph (265 km/h).

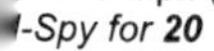

*I-Spy for **20***

Marcos Mantula Spyder
The Marcos Mantula, powered by a Rover 3.9-litre V8 engine, shares many of its features with its 2-litre, Ford-engined cousin. In the Spyder, the convertible body shell is moulded from fibreglass on a steel chassis. The car has been designed to suit drivers of almost any height, and there is a unique pedal assembly to vary the legroom.
I-Spy for ***25***

Mini Marcos
This uniquely styled little coupé may be fitted with either a 1.3- or a 1.0-litre engine and both will run on unleaded fuel. The car is just 1 metre (39 inches) high and only 3.45 metres (11 ft 4 in) long. The coachwork is reinforced fibreglass.
I-Spy for ***25***

Mazda MX-3

This car has been designed to compete head on with leading 'hot hatchbacks'. It was conceived from scratch as a 2+2 sports coupé. It is powered by either what was claimed to be the world's smallest V-6 engine, a 1.8-litre unit, or a 1.6-litre, fuel-injected engine. The V6 gives 0-62 mph (0-100 km/h) in 8.5 seconds and a top speed of 126 mph (202 km/h).

I-Spy for ***10***

Mazda MX-5

This is an attempt to merge classic European style with ultra-modern technology. It is front engined but rear-wheel drive, and there is a soft folding top. It is powered by a 1.6-litre, 16-valve engine. The car is designed to be lightweight yet rigid, and the weight has been distributed evenly.

I-Spy for ***15***

Mazda MX-6

This is a two-door, sports coupé powered by either a 2.0-litre, fuel-injected, 16-valve engine or a 2.5-litre, 24-valve, V6 — both specially developed for the car. Mazda claims to use environmentally friendly technology by including large amounts of recyclable materials in its construction.

*I-Spy for **15***

Mazda RX-7

Like its predecessors, Mazda's latest sports car is powered by a two-rotor rotary engine. Many of the parts which go to make up this engine were also included in the unit contained in the Mazdaspeed 787B which won the 1991 Le Mans 24-hour Race. To reduce weight, thermoplastics and aluminium have been used wherever practicable.

*I-Spy for **20***

MGA 1600 MkII Roadster

The MGA was a completely new design, and broke away from the traditional pre-war sports car shape of the TD range. As with most MGs, this car was used in competition work, as a team car and in private hands. The top speed was 101 mph (163 km/h). This is a 1962 model.

*I-Spy for **20***

Mini Cooper

The BMC Mini, designed by Alec Issigonis, first appeared in 1959 and it is still with us. Produced by Rover, today's Mini Cooper 1.3i is powered by a fuel-injected 1275 cc 63PS engine that offers 0-60 mph (0-96 km/h) in 11.5 seconds, yet it still returns over 36 mpg (13 km/l) around town and almost 50 mpg (17.7 km/l) at a constant 56 mph (90 km/h).

*I-Spy for **10***

Mitsubishi Space Runner/Space Wagon

This is the latest generation of Mitsubishi's so-called 'people carriers' or MPVs. They are practical alternatives to conventional estates. They are powered by a 1.8-litre, 16-valve, fuel-injected engine developing 121 bhp and giving a top speed of over 112 mph (180 km/h). The Space Runner is a five seater while the Wagon can accomodate seven. What does MPV stand for?

I-Spy for ***5*** *— double with answer* multi purpose veichle ✓

Mitsubishi Sigma

Aimed at the executive ca market, this well-appointe saloon is driven by a 3-litre, V6, 24-valve, fuel-injected engine which develops 202 bhp and wil take the car to 140 mph (225 km/h) where allowed It has ABS, an integrated handling system which includes 4-wheel steering, and electronic control suspension.

I-Spy for ***10***

Morris Bullnose Saloon

Cycle man, William Morris, built his first 'Bullnose' production model in 1912. By 1926, the car was extremely popular and had a larger, 1550 cc engine. Many of these cars survive today and there is a thriving owners' club.

I-Spy for ***30***

Nash Metropolitan Convertible

This car resulted from an agreement between Nash in the United States and Austin in England. Engine and components were made up from Austin A40 and A30 parts. The 1500 cc engine gave a top speed of 72 mph (116 km/h). This is a 1954 model and its new price was £516.00.

I-Spy for ***30***

Nissan 100NX

This is a sporting 2+2 in which the rear seat folds down to provide extra luggage space when needed. It is powered by a twin-cam, 16-valve, 1.6-litre engine to give 0-62 mph (0-100 km/h) performance of 10.7 seconds. The T-bar roof windows lift off for those times when the weather is suitable for open-air driving.
*I-Spy for **15***

Nissan 200SX

The 1.8-litre, twin cam, turbo-charged, 16-valve engine with inter-cooler offers 0-62 mph (0-110 km/h) performance of 7.3 seconds and a top speed of 137 mph (220 km/h) where permissible. Even around town however, the car is still capable of fuel economy of almost 26 mpg (9.2 km/l). Multi-link suspension, ABS, and power steering are standard.
*I-Spy for **15***

Nissan 300ZX

Nissan claims that this is 'the definitive sports car of its time'. It is powered by a 3.0-litre, 24-valve, twin cam, turbocharged V6 engine capable of taking the car from 0-62 mph (0-100 km/h) in just 5.9 seconds and on to a maximum speed of 155 mph (250 km/h) where permitted. Its interior has been designed so that it seems to wrap around the driver and passengers for safety and comfort.
*I-Spy for **20***

Peugeot 106

Launched at the 1991 Motorfair, the 106 is Peugeot's most compact design, at under 3.6 metres (less than 12 ft) in overall length. There are four models and a total of eleven versions available, ranging from the 1.0-litre XN to the 1.4 XSi Catalyst which has a top speed of 118 mph (190 km/h) yet still returns 38.7 mpg (13.7 km/l) at 75 mph (120 km/h).
*I-Spy for **5***

Porsche 356 Speedster

Designed by the same Dr Porsche who had produced the people's car, the Volkswagen Beetle, the 356 was the first Porsche sports car. It had a 1600 cc engine, cost £1891.00 and could reach 101 mph (163 km/h). This is a 1955 example.
*I-Spy for **30***

Porsche 911 Carrera 2 Cabriolet Turbo Look

This limited-edition Porsche combines the normally aspirated engine of the Carrera 2 with the wide wheel arches, brakes and suspension of the high-performance 911 Turbo. The 3.6-litre, air-cooled, 6-cylinder engine develops 250 bhp.
I-Spy for ***25***

Porsche 911 Carrera RS

This two-door coupé is the first production sports car from Porsche to be given the 'RS' since the 911 Carrera 2.7- and 3-litre models in the early 1970s. The 'RS' indicates light weight and high power. The 3.6-litre, air-cooled, 260-bhp engine takes the car from a standing start to 62 mph (100 km/h) in 5.3 seconds.
I-Spy for ***20***

Porsche 968

This car is available in either coupé or cabriolet versions and is typical of modern Porches with large, round, pop-up headlights, sloping bonnet, and curved wings. Its 16-valve, 4-cylinder, 3-litre engine develops 240 bhp to give a top speed of 153 mph (246 km/h) where conditions allow.
I-Spy for ***25***

Proton 'Triple Valve'

There are twelve models of saloons and so-called 'Aerobacks' in the Proton range. They are fitted with 1.3- or 1.5-litre, 4-cylinder, 12-valve engines from Mitsubishi. All cars are fitted with a 5-speed manual gearbox and there is the option of a 3-speed, automatic transmission on the SE saloon. Both engines run on either leaded or unleaded fuel.
*I-Spy for **10***

Reliant Rialto/Robin

Reliant has been building specialist transport since 1935 when the company developed a van with motor cycle front forks. The current range of 3-wheelers comes in six models: the Rialto 2- and 3-door versions, together with a van; Rialto 2- and 3-door SEs; and the Robin LX. All are powered by the Reliant-designed 848-cc, 4-cylinder engine. The body is moulded from GRP.
What do the letters GRP stand for?
*I-Spy for **10** — double with answer* ______________________

Renault 4TL

More than 5 000 000 Renault 4s were built at the company's factory in Billencourt. Some people thought of them as Renault's answer to the Citroën 2CV. Very much a utility car, its best top speed was 72 mph (116 km/h)

*I-Spy for **15***

Renault Clio

Another 'supermini' from the famous French manufacturer, the Clio has a distinctive style and sleek, slippery shape. For a small car, it has an extra-long wheelbase and wide track. There are thirteen models in the range from the 1.2-litre, 3/5 -door RL to the potent 16-Valve with a top speed of 130 mph (209 km/h) where permissible.

*I-Spy for **5***

Renault 19 16-valve

This high-performance version of the Renault 19 range of family cars comes in both saloon and hatchback versions. The 1.8-litre, 16-valve engine develops 137 bhp and powers the car from 0-62 mph (0-100 km/h) in only 8.5 seconds. Where conditions allow, the top speed is 132 mph (212 km/h).
*I-Spy for **15***

Renault Espace

With its redesigned exterior and the newly available 2.9-litre, V6, 153-bhp engine, the Espace continues to build upon its reputation as a versatile, executive people carrier. Though the standard specifications are comprehensive, the options include ABS, air conditioning, and self-levelling suspension.
*I-Spy for **10***

Rolls-Royce Silver Spur II

The total production rate is about twenty-five cars a year, so this luxurious touring limousine must be one of the world's most exclusive cars. Cocktail cabinet with crystal fittings, a CD player, television, refrigerator unit, veneered picnic tables, and cellular telephone are standard.
*I-Spy for **50***

Rover 400

There are eleven models ir the 400 series of medium-sized luxury saloons. They range from the 414Si 16v with its 1396-cc, K-series engine to the lively 420GSi Sport with its 2-litre MI6i, fuel-injected engine which can take the car from 0-60 mph (0-96 mph) in under 8 seconds and on to 127 mp (204 km/h) where permissible.
I-Spy for ***5***

Rover 800

All ten models of Rover's flagship range are offered in either saloon or fastback versions. The luxury 800 is aimed at the executive car market and now features the distinctive Rover grill. The 820i offers a fuel economy of 38.8 mpg (13.76 km/l) at a constant 75 mph (120 km/h). The Vitesse has a top speed of 137 mph (220 km/h) where permitted.
I-Spy for ***5***

SAAB 96

The Swedish aircraft company began manufacturing cars in 1950. Increasingly successful at rallying, early 96s had two-stroke 841 cc engines. The low-drag shape helped the cars attain a top speed of 76 mph (123 km/h). This is a 1966 model.
*I-Spy for **15***

SAAB 9000 CS

The second generation SAAB 9000 is a five-door car which aims to offer the refined ride and noise qualities of a four-door saloon. With their usual attention to safety, SAAB supplies ABS brakes as standard across the whole catalyst range. There are nine models and four 16-valve engines with the 2.3-litre turbo-charged unit developing 220 bhp.
*I Spy for **10***

Sao Penza

Manufactured by the South African Motor Corporation, the Penza promises Japanese-style technology and build quality in a family car at competitive prices. There is a 5-door hatchback and a 4-door saloon, both powered by a 1.3-litre engine. The hatchback achieves 42.8 mpg (15.18 km/l) at 75 mph (120 km/h).
*I-Spy for **15***

Skoda Favorit Estate

Continuing Skoda's tradition of offering value-for-money motoring, the Favorit Estate is the company's first estate model since the Octavia in 1971. The engine is the familiar 1289 cc, 4-cylinder, transverse unit which will run on leaded o unleaded fuel, and there is a 5-speed gearbox.

I-Spy for ***10***

Subaru Legacy 2.0

Two new engines and revised front and rear body styling have been included with the launch of the 2.0 MPFi GL 4WD and the high-performance 2.0 CAM Turbo 4WD saloons and estates. The 4-wheel drive gives the cars off-road capability. The rally-proven Turbo will take even the estate to 137 mph (220 km/h) where permissible.

I-Spy for ***10***

Suzuki Vitara

A 5-door estate version ha been added to the range c 4-wheel-drive Vitaras. And the 3-door models now feature a more powerful 1.6-litre engine with a thre way catalytic converter. Th 5-door vehicle is driven by 1.6-litre, 16-valve engine delivering 95 bhp, and it also has a larger fuel tank than its smaller cousin.

I-Spy for ***10***

Toyota Camry

Flagship of the Toyota range, the Camry boasts engines mounted on hydraulic fluid-filled mounts to reduce noise. The car has ABS as well as an anti-dive suspension system to make it even more stable on hard braking. The V6 GX has a 3-litre, 24 valve, 185 bhp engine giving a top speed of 134 mph (215 km/h).
*I-Spy for **10***

Toyota Celica GT-Four

This car was developed from the GT-Four that won the 1990 World Rally Championship. The 2.0-litre, fuel-injected, turbocharged engine delivers 201 bhp to accelerate the car to 60 mph (96 km/h) in under 8 seconds and, where permissible, a top speed of 143 mph (230 km/h). Pictured is the Carlos Sainz edition, limited to 5000.
*I-Spy for **25** — double for Carlos Sainz Edition*

Toyota Landcruiser

Toyota claims that their Landcruiser is the most popular 4-wheel drive vehicle in the world. The VX version has a 4.2-litre turbo-diesel engine developing 165 bhp so that it can tow weights of 3500 kilograms with little effort. The short wheelbase Landcruiser II has a 2.4-litre turbo-diesel unit and switchable 2- or 4-wheel drive.

*I-Spy for **15***

Toyota Previa

High-lift rear door, wide sliding passenger door, and a cavernous interior achieved by tilting the engine 75° to one side and mounting it under the floor, combine to make the Previa one of the most versatile MPVs of its class. It boasts a 2.4-litre, fuel-injected engine capable of 32.8 mpg (11.6 km/l) at a steady 56 mph (90 km/h).

*I-Spy for **10***

Toyota Sera

This has been designed as an urban sports car. It has a 1.5-litre engine developing 110 bhp. Its futuristic design features gull-wing doors, glass roof, and automatic air conditioning. Note: Toyota (GB) Ltd does not market this vehicle and it wishes to point out that using it in Britain could be illegal.

*I-Spy for **50***

Triumph TR7 Drophead
TR7s were very different in styling from earlier TRs. Some enthusiasts called it a 'hairdresser's car', but it soon proved its worth in events such as the Manx International Trophy and Lombard RAC Rally. This one is from 1980.
*I-Spy for **20***

Triumph Vitesse
The Herald and Vitesse represented a new departure for Triumph in that they were styled by the Italian designer Michelotti. The 6-cylinder Vitesse was launched in May 1962 in saloon or convertible form. It was a very quick car with 0-60 mph (0-96 km/h) performance of 15.5 seconds.
*I-Spy for **20***

TVR Griffith

This is a 2-seater, 2-door, convertible sports car with a glass-reinforced resin body shell on a tubular steel frame backbone chassis. The 4-litre, alloy V8 engine delivers 240 bhp to give the car 0-60 mph (0-96 km/h) performance in under 5 seconds and a top speed of 150 mph (240 km/h) under acceptable conditions.
*I-Spy for **25***

TVRV8S

This is a handcrafted sportscar which offers the same engine and performance as the TVR Griffith but in a more traditional, 'classic' package. The cockpit options include full hide trim, a leather-rimmed steering wheel, and Wilton carpets.
*I-Spy for **25***

Vauxhall Astra

There are no less than sixteen models in the Astra range of 3/5-door hatchbacks and estates. The 1.4 Merits offer unleaded fuel economy of up to 42.6 mpg (15.1 km/l) at 75 mph (120 km/h) while the top-of-the-range 2.0i 16-valve hatch has a top speed of 137 mph (220 km/h) and a 0-62 mph (0-100 km/h) time of 8 seconds.
*I-Spy for **5***

Vauxhall Frontera

There are 4-door and 2-door models in the range: the Sport has removable rear side windows, tailgate glass, and rear roof section. The Sport, with its selectable 4-wheel drive is powered by a 2.0-litre, fuel-injected engine, while the extended wheelbase Frontera has 2.4i petrol or 2.3 turbo-diesel engine options.
*I-Spy for **10***

Vauxhall Senator

The Vauxhall Senator is a 4-door luxury saloon available with a choice of three 6-cylinder engines to give a 4-model range: the 2.6i, 3.0i, CD, and CD24v. Full leather trim and air conditioning are standard on the two CD models as is the 'electronic ride control system'. ABS is fitted to all models.
*I-Spy for **5***

Volkswagen Corrado G60

There are two models in the 3-door Corrado hatchback range — the 16V and the G60, both powered by 1.8-litre, transverse engines. The 16V develops 136 bhp while supercharging increases the G60's output to 160 bhp and gives a top speed of 140 mph (225 km/h) where conditions allow.
I-Spy for ***10***

Volkswagen Golf

The 1992 Golf comes in three models: the Ryder, Driver, and GTD with the first two available in 3- and 5-door versions. The Ryder has a 1.6-litre engine, the Driver a 1.8-, and the GTD a 1.6-litre turbocharged diesel unit. Catalytic converters are optional. At a constant 56 mph (90 km/h), the Ryder returns 48.7 mpg (17.3 km/l).
I-Spy for ***5***

Volkswagen Polo

The latest range of VW Polos includes three hatchbacks, four coupés, and a 1.3-litre saloon car. The most fuel-efficient vehicles in the range are 1.3 CL coupé, hatchback, and saloon which return figures of almost 35 mpg (12.4 km/l) in town and 56.5 mpg (20 km/l) at a constant 56 mph (90 km/h).
I-Spy for ***5***

Volvo 960

Volvo's latest luxury saloon is offered with either a 2.3-litre, 4-cylinder, turbo-charged engine or a 2.9-litre, 6-cylinder, 24-valve, fuel-injected unit. Well known for safety, Volvo's new feature, SIPS, absorbs the impact of a side collision. What does SIPS stand for?

____

I-Spy for ***5***
Double with answer

Wolseley 1500 Saloon

Wolseley began as a sheep-shearing factory in 1896. By the 1960s, they were part of the Austin/ Morris British Motor Company. The 1500 was originally designed as a replacement for the Morris Minor. Another version of it was the Riley 1.5. This car is from 1962.

I-Spy for ***20***

Yugo

Yugo Cars began trading in the United Kingdom in 1981. The latest Tempo range of front-wheel drive hatchbacks includes six inexpensive models. Engines range from 903 cc, through 1100 cc, to 1300 cc. The 1.3LS, develops 65 bhp although it still achieves 0-60 mph (0-96 km/h) in 11.3 seconds.

I-Spy for ***15***

INDEX

Answers
Alfa Romeo 75: two spark plugs per cylinder.
Aston Martin DB5: revolutions per minute.
Aston Martin Virage Volante 2+2: brake horse power.
Audi 80: 4-wheel drive.
Honda Concerto: anti-lock braking system.
Mitsubishi Space Runner: multi-purpose vehicle.
Reliant Rialto: glass-reinforced plastic.
Volvo 960: side-impact protection system.

© I-Spy Limited 1992

ISBN (paperback) 1 85671 119 6

Michelin Tyre Public Limited Company
Davy House, Lyon Road, Harrow, Middlesex HA1 2DQ

MICHELIN and the Michelin Man are Registered Trademarks of Michelin

All rights reserved. No part of this publication may be reproduced, stored in a retrieval system, or transmitted in any form or by any means, electronic, mechanical photocopying or otherwise without the prior written permission of I-Spy Limited.

A CIP record for this title is available from the British Library.

Edited and designed by Curtis Garratt Limited, The Old Vicarage, Horton cum Studley, Oxford OX9 1BT

The Publisher gratefully acknowledges the contribution of the motor car manufacturers whose cars are described in this book and who provided the majority of the photographs. Additional photographs by National Motor Museum, Beaulieu; Neil Curtis. Cover photograph: Richard Garratt. Title page photograph: Jaguar Cars Ltd.

Colour reproduction by Norwich Litho Services Limited.

Printed in Spain.